Party P

by Joan Freese
Photographs by Gregg Andersen

Developed for Harcourt, Inc., by Gareth Stevens, Inc.
This edition published by Harcourt, Inc., by agreement with Gareth Stevens, Inc. No part of this publication may be reproduced or transmitted in any form or by any means, electronic or mechanical, including photocopy, recording, or any information storage and retrieval system, without permission in writing from the copyright holder.

Requests for permission to make copies of any part of the work should be addressed to Permissions Department, Gareth Stevens, Inc., 330 West Olive Street, Suite 100, Milwaukee, Wisconsin 53212. Fax: 414-332-3567.

HARCOURT and the Harcourt Logo are trademarks of Harcourt, Inc., registered in the United States of America and/or other jurisdictions.

Printed in Mexico

ISBN 13: 978-0-15-360229-0
ISBN 10: 0-15-360229-5

3 4 5 6 7 8 9 10 050 16 15 14 13 12 11 10 09 08

Harcourt
SCHOOL PUBLISHERS

Chapter 1:
Party Prep

Mr. Kent's class is having a party. They will mark the 100th day of school. Everyone will help plan! The class will decide what to do at the party. They will decide what food to eat, too.

Children will bring things for the party.
Teams can use math to help them plan.
If they plan, they will bring just the right
amount of things.

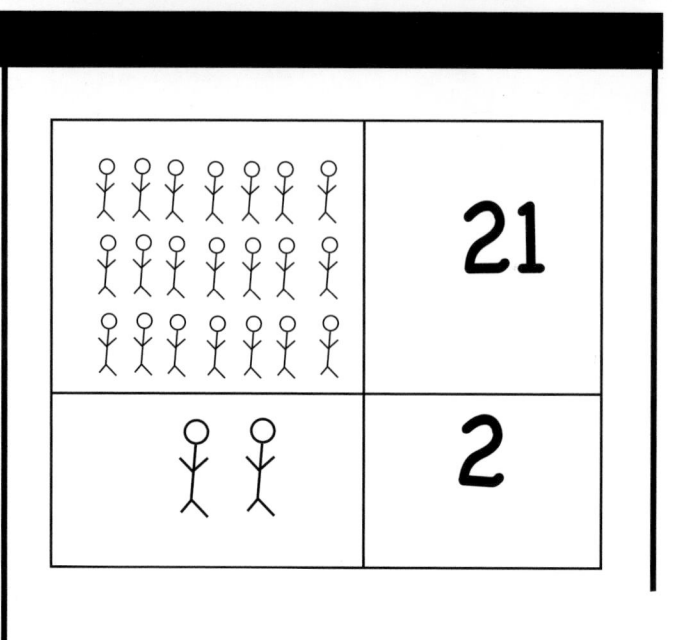

How many people will be at the party? There are 21 children. There will be 2 adults. Mr. Kent will be at the party. There will also be a guest.

The class writes a number sentence. They add.

21 + 2 = 23

The sum is the number of people who will be at the party.

There will be 23 people in all. The class needs to bring enough food for 23 people. They need to bring enough drinks for everyone, too.

Chapter 2:
Time to Get Busy

Team One will bring muffins. Cindy will bring 12 muffins. Molly will bring some, too. She will bring 14 muffins. How many muffins will they bring in all?

They add to find the answer.

12 + 14 = 26

They will have 26 muffins for the party. What kind of muffins should they bring? Cindy likes oat muffins. Molly likes blueberry.

$$\begin{array}{r} 12 \\ + 14 \\ \hline 26 \end{array}$$

Team Two will bring boxes of juice. Chase has a pack that had 36 boxes. The pack is open now. His family drank 11 boxes. They were thirsty! How many boxes are left?

They subtract.

36 − 11 = 25

There are 25 boxes of juice left. That should be enough juice. There are many kinds of juice in the pack. Everyone will find juice they like to drink.

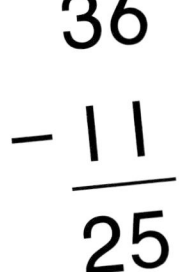

$$\begin{array}{r} 36 \\ -\ 11 \\ \hline 25 \end{array}$$

Chapter 3:
More Work to Do

Team Three will bring balloons. Jordan has 24 blue balloons. Seth has 17 orange ones. Jordan's balloons are left over from a picnic. They had extra ones. His dad saved them in a box. Now Jordan can use them for the party.

How many balloons do they have in all?
They add.

$24 + 17 = 41$

They will have 41 balloons. Seth's mom will help them blow up the balloons. His mom will bring them to the party. She will bring them in the morning. She cannot stay for the party though. She has to go to work.

$$
\begin{array}{r}
1 \\
24 \\
+\ 17 \\
\hline
41
\end{array}
$$

The children will string beads at the party. The art teacher has cord they can use. Team Four has 9 packs of long beads. They have 21 packs of round beads. How many more packs of round beads than long beads are there?

They subtract to find the answer.

21 – 9 = 12

There are 12 more packs of round beads than long beads. There are plenty of beads in all to use at the party.

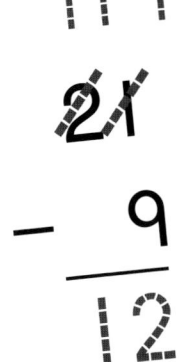

Chapter 4:
Party Time!

Today is the 100th day of school. Time for party fun! The principal is here. Her name is Ms. Brown. Welcome, Ms. Brown! She is the special guest.

Each child counts 100 beads. The children
string the beads. They make things to wear.
Some children will give their beads to friends.

Mr. Kent has a question. There are five teams. Four teams have done a job for the party. How many teams have not done a job?

That is easy! The children do the math in their heads. Four teams have done jobs. One team has not done a job. That team is ready to work now!

Team Five is excited. They listen to Mr. Kent. What is their job? He tells them it is an important job. It is also fun to do.

They will help serve juice and muffins. Let's go, Team Five! Everyone is hungry! The class eats muffins. They drink juice. Some children talk about their beads. They show Ms. Brown what they made.

It is time to clean up. The children throw
away the trash. They wipe the tables clean.
Good work!

The children had fun stringing beads.
They liked their snacks and juice. Everyone
had a great time. The class cannot wait to
use math to plan another party!

Glossary

add to join 2 groups

number sentence 21 + 2 = 23 is a number sentence.
36 − 11 = 25 is also a number sentence.

subtract to take away objects from a group or to compare groups